this is a house

---

draw the house

colour it in

write

this is a house

next to the house there is a garden

this is the garden

---

draw the garden

colour it in

write

this is a garden

in this garden there is a tree

this is the tree

---

draw the tree

colour it in

write

this is the tree

there is a mattress
under the tree

this mattress is yellow

---

write

under the tree is a mattress

there is a fuzzbuzz
next to the mattress

this is the fuzzbuzz

---

draw the mattress

colour it yellow

draw the fuzzbuzz next to it

write
this is the fuzzbuzz

the fuzzbuzz is in the garden

he lives there

he lives in the mattress
under the tree

---

write

he lives in the mattress

the fuzzbuzz jumps up

he jumps up on the mattress

up and down

up and down

up and down he goes

this is good fun

**draw and colour the fuzzbuzz
jumping on the yellow mattress**

write

he jumps on the mattress

and next the fuzzbuzz
goes up into the tree

---

draw the fuzzbuzz in the tree

write

the fuzzbuzz is in the tree

down drops the fuzzbuzz

down and down he drops

he drops down to the mattress

---

draw the fuzzbuzz jumping down

write

the fuzzbuzz drops down

down to the mattress

drops the fuzzbuzz

up and down he goes

jumping is fun

it is good fun

---

draw this

write

jumping is good fun

the fuzzbuzz goes to sleep

he goes to sleep
on the yellow mattress

---

draw this and colour it in

write
the fuzzbuzz goes to sleep